Night Post

Benjamin Read & Laura Trinder

First published 2014
By Improper Books
An Imprint of Read Publishing, Ltd
Home Farm, 44 Evesham Road, Cookhill
Alcester, Warwickshire, B49 5LJ
www.improperbooks.com

Story: Benjamin Read
Illustrator: Laura Trinder
Design: Zoë Horn Haywood
Managing Editor: Matt Gibbs

To the Pook, as ever. You even make an appearance in this one.
- Benjamin Read

For my family, old and new.
- Laura Trinder

ISBN: 978-1-4733-2028-4

Printed and bound in the United Kingdom.

'At Midnight, when all good folk
should be abed, the Night Post
rides forth to serve the dead.'

- Victorian Children's Verse

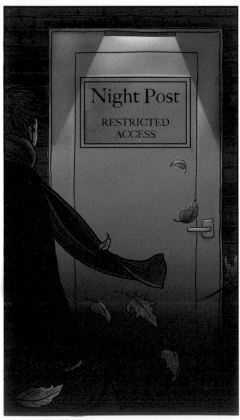

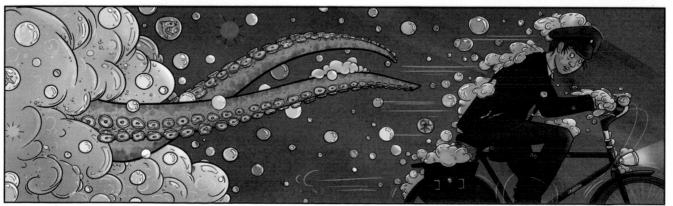

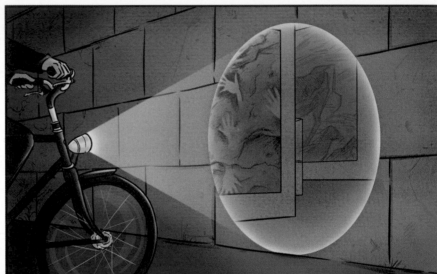

Disturb Not
The
Dreamless Sleep
Eternal

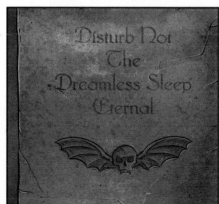

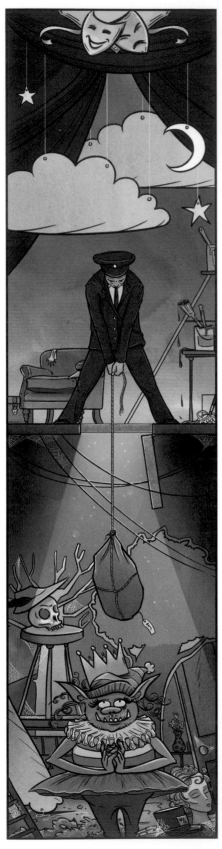

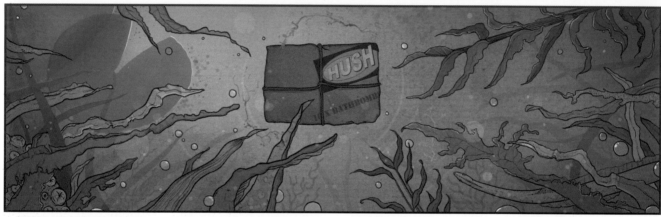

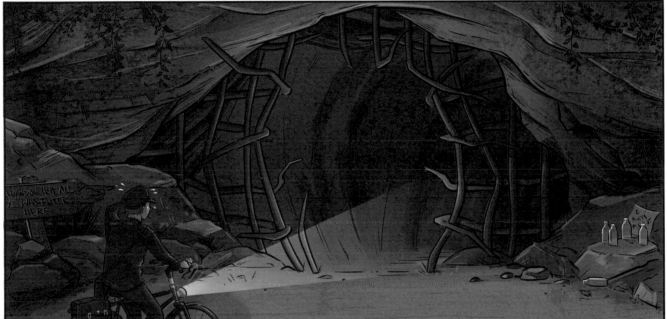

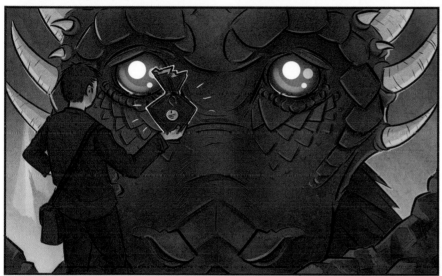

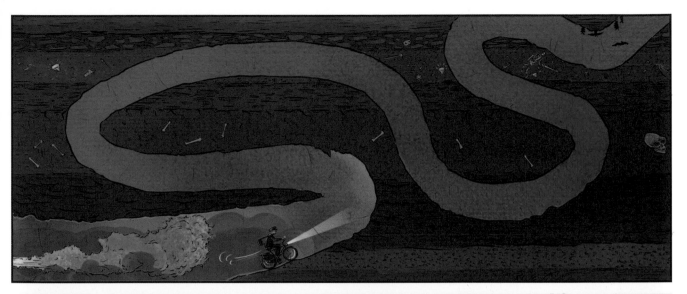

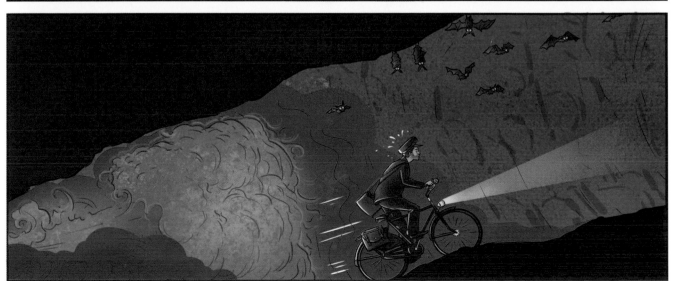

Benjamin Read writes comics and makes films. He wrote the multiply award-nominated PORCELAIN: A GOTHIC FAIRY TALE, the silent comic BUTTERFLY GATE, and children's book, NIGHT POST, as well as the TRUE GRIT and SUPER 8 comic adaptations. He also wrote and produced the films ARMISTICE and 500 MILES NORTH. He is one of the founder members of the Improper Books comics collective, and is fuelled principally by tea and whimsy. He is currently working on the rest of the Porcelain sequence, alongside writing the next piece of illustrated spooky mischief with Laura Trinder.

Website: benjaminread.co.uk
Twitter: @Bookpirate

Laura Trinder is a freelance illustrator, bookseller, and co-founder of Improper Books. Her days consist of reading, recommending, and creating books, which for a book-lover isn't half bad. As a member of the Improper Books studio, she is working on comics and picture books for younger readers. Night Post is her first venture into the world of sequential art.

Website: lauratrinder.co.uk
Twitter: @xbirdyblue

Improper Books is a comic and graphic novel studio focusing on stories that have a touch of the fairy tale, the Gothic or the macabre.

Website: improperbooks.com
Twitter: @ImproperBooks